HELLO HAPPY!

AN ACTIVITY BOOK FOR YOUNG PEOPLE WHO SOMETIMES FEEL SAD OR ANGRY

STUDIO PRESS

First published in the UK in 2017 by Studio Press Books,
an imprint of Bonnier Books UK
The Plaza, 535 King's Road, London, SW10 0SZ
www.studiopressbooks.co.uk
www.bonnierbooks.co.uk

Consultant Dr. Sharie Coombes, Child, Family & Adult Psychotherapist,
Ed.D, MA (PsychPsych), DHypPsych(UK), Senior QHP, B.Ed.

10 9 8 7 6 5

978-1-78370-899-4

Written by Stephanie Clarkson
Illustrated by Katie Abey
Designed by Rob Ward

Printed in the United Kingdom

Lots of children need a bit of extra help every now and then, and here are 2 organisations you can turn to if you don't want to talk to people you know. They have helped thousands of children with every imaginable problem and will know how to help you.

CHILDLINE

Help and advice about a wide range of issues.

Comforts, advises and protects children 24 hours a day and offers free confidential counselling by helpline, online chat and Ask Sam.

Tel: 0800 1111   www.childline.org.uk

THE SAMARITANS

The Samaritans – Listening and support for anyone who needs it.

Contact 24 hours a day, 365 days a year – calls and emails are free and confidential. If you need a response immediately, it's best to call on the phone.

Email: jo@samaritans.org
Tel: 116 123 (24 hours)   www.samaritans.org

HEAD AND HEART

We all have emotions. Happiness, sadness, anger, fear, surprise and disgust are basic instincts - reactions to chemicals being released into our bodies and brains.

Emotions are very useful because they influence the way we behave. For example if we feel afraid, we try and get away from the danger. If we feel happy, we relax. While our ancestors relied on their emotions to help them stay alive, today we can use emotions to help us manage and plan our lives.

Emotions can happen to us quickly but the good news is that we can work on and even change our feelings. Feelings result from emotions and are specific to you. They depend on:

...what has happened to you in your life

...the way you feel about yourself

...your temperament and how you deal with emotions

While emotions are fleeting chemical reactions which cause short-lived physical changes throughout the body, feelings can last for hours, days, weeks, months or even years.

We can sense our emotions from the time we are tiny babies. At first we react to them with simple facial expressions or actions like smiling, laughing or crying. As we grow up however, we become better at knowing what we are feeling and putting the feeling into words.

Learning to recognize our emotions in this way and more importantly learning to manage the resulting feelings is very important. It's called 'emotional intelligence' and it helps us to build relationships, resolve arguments and move on from past difficult feelings and therefore succeed and be happy in life.

Reading this book and doing some or all of the activities will help you to make friends with your emotions and learn to deal with your feelings so that you can stay happy and positive.

So come on,
what have you got to lose?
Turn the page and say 'Hello happy!'

I'M FEELING KINDA...

How are you feeling? Whether you're angry, sad or full of joy, it's okay. All emotions are okay – which is a good thing as we have loads of them!

Grab a pen and draw the expression to fit the emotion or add the emotion to fit the expression.

I'M FEELING

Happy
....

I'M FEELING

....

I'M FEELING

....

I'M FEELING

....

I'M FEELING

Sad

....

I'M FEELING

....

I'M FEELING

....

embarrassed

shocked

frustrated

angry   shy

scared

lonely   tired

anxious

 **BRAIN BREAK!**

To listen to your emotions and feelings you need to quiet your mind. To do this you need to give your brain a break by switching off from the every day things which buzz around cluttering up your head.

The first thing to do is to get rid of the noise around you and learn to like silence. It may feel uncomfortable at first, but here's what you need to do:

Turn off the TV.

 Turn off any video games.

 Turn off any radios or stereos.

Put smart technology, phones, tablets etc away.

Close windows to the outside world so you can't hear car engines and sirens.

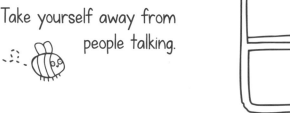 Take yourself away from people talking.

Once you've done this...

Sit still in a comfortable position, close your eyes and concentrate on breathing in and out, in and out.

Now, in this quiet, calm state ask yourself how you are feeling.

Give yourself the chance to recognize any underlying feelings of anger, sadness, worry or unease, and give yourself permission to feel that feeling.

For example say,

"I am feeling SAD. I feel SAD because I had a bad day at school. I will not always feel SAD, but right now I feel SAD and that is OK."

Repeat this several times.

FEELING FEELINGS

Sometimes your feelings don't want to stay inside. Sometimes they want to **JUMP AND BURST OUT.**

Write where and how you feel when you're angry on this dummy.

Write where and how you feel when you're sad on this dummy.

MY BEATING HEART

Take some time to get to know your heart rate. Take your pulse by holding the two fingers nearest your thumb to your neck or to the underside of your wrist.

Like all emotions, anger releases chemicals in your brain, which then cause changes in your body that you can feel. One of these changes is an increased heart rate.

TRY TAKING YOUR PULSE WHEN YOU HAVE...

JUST WOKEN UP   RUN ON THE SPOT FOR 3 MINUTES

HAD A ROW WITH SOMEONE

EATEN A BIG MEAL

JUST BEGUN A PIECE OF HOMEWORK

READ A CHAPTER OF A BOOK

BEEN FOR A WALK

Write down the beats per minute for each of these.

REMEMBER! Anger can be positive. Many people have made good changes in the world because they felt so angry about something they used the anger to spur them on to positive action. What makes you angry in the world? How could you make a difference?

DID YOU KNOW? Your heart rate will also increase when you are stressed or afraid.

THE ANGER ICEBERG

Anger never exists on its own – there are always underlying emotions causing it. Add more emotions to the underwater part of the iceberg to show the other emotions which might lead to you feeling angry.

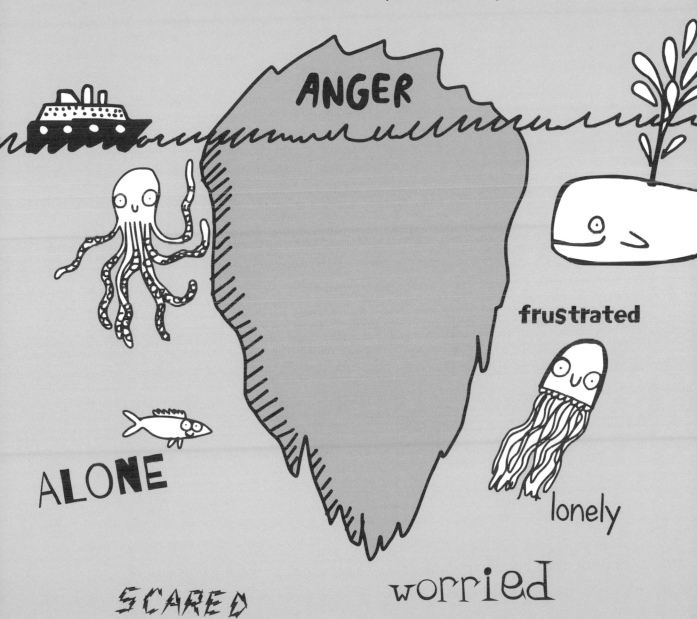

OFF THE RECORD

An increased heart rate is just one of the warning signs which show you're feeling angry. Circle any warning signs you recognize or have experienced.

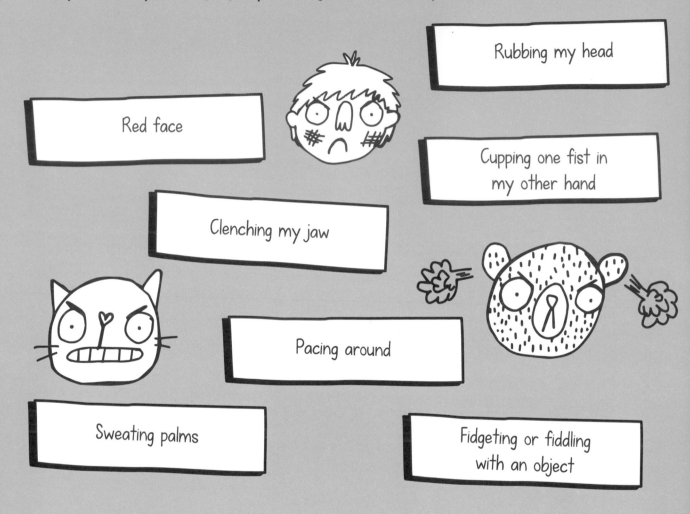

Rubbing my head

Red face

Cupping one fist in my other hand

Clenching my jaw

Pacing around

Sweating palms

Fidgeting or fiddling with an object

Think hard about how you look and feel right before you lose your temper.
If you're not sure, ask someone close to you and who you trust to describe
how you look or what you do when you're about to get angry.
Learning to spot these signs is vital if you are going to learn to control your temper.

EMOTIONS LTD

Sadness and anger often go hand-in-hand.

For example, you might be feeling sad at not having been picked for the school football team and as a result angrily say something mean to a friend who did make the team.

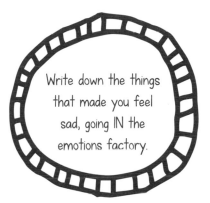

Write down the things that made you feel sad, going IN the emotions factory.

If these made you do something in anger, write what you did, coming OUT of the factory.

IN →

OUT →

FACE YOUR FEELINGS

How do you look and feel when an emotion takes over? Pick up your pen and add yourself to the photo frames and then write down the kind of things you sometimes say or do when you are full of anger or sadness.

Draw yourself when you are feeling angry.

When I am angry I say

....

....

When I am angry I

....

....

Draw yourself when you are feeling sad.

When I am sad I say

....
....

When I am sad I

....
....

ROGUES' GALLERY

How would 'anger' and 'sadness' look if they were cartoon characters? Use this space and your incredible imagination to bring these key emotions to life.

Are your characters monsters, droopy-eared dogs or crazy-looking plants?

Do they have teeth, fur, scales or feathers?

What are your creatures called? You could name them Angroid and Sadro, or perhaps Gary and Kenneth. Once you've decided, be sure to introduce yourself.

Do they have fur, teeth or scales? What colour are they?

What next? Try making your creation from modelling clay.

HOT, HOT, HOT!

Anger is like a boiling kettle. One minute it's simmering, the next steam is coming out of your ears. Use the thermometer below to write down examples of times when you've felt the different levels of anger.

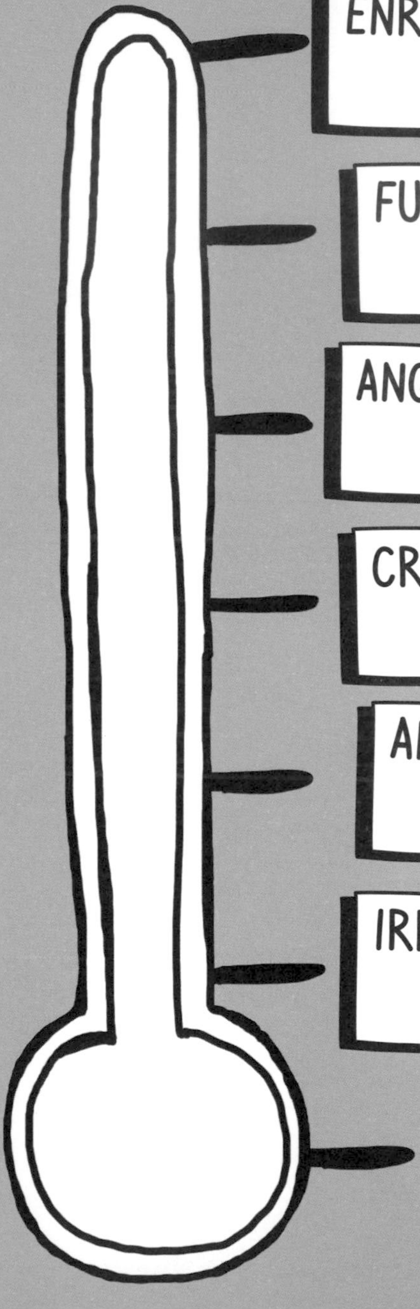

ENRAGED

FURIOUS

ANGRY

CROSS

ANNOYED

IRRITATED

CALM

FEELING RUBBISH?

What emotions or feelings could these be?

ANGER

worry

FLOOD OF FURY

It's important not to keep your anger bottled up until it gets out of control.

Imagine the things which make you angry flooding out. Draw or write them below.

Letting anger out in a controlled way will allow it to flow away safely.

TiCK TiCK BOOM!

The next time you feel like you might explode with anger, try one of the following techniques to control your temper or maybe add your own idea to this page.

Once you've tried it, give the strategy a score out of 10 to show how helpful it was.

Anger is a natural emotion. Everyone gets angry, we need to know how to control explosions of anger as aggressive behaviour is not okay.

/ 10	Bounce really hard on a trampoline.
/ 10	Snap a pencil.
/ 10	Sing to some really loud music.
/ 10	Pummel a cushion.
/ 10	Do 50 star jumps.
/ 10	Do a crazy dance.
/ 10	Scream really loudly into a small space, like an airing cupboard.
/ 10	
/ 10	Scribble really hard in a notebook.
/ 10	
/ 10	Run on the spot or up and down the garden as fast as you can for 3 minutes.
/ 10	

I'M SO MAD I COULD...

Use your imagination to finish this sentence starter.

...crush a grape

...HOWL LIKE A WEREWOLF

...wrestle an octopus

I'm so mad I could...

I'm so mad I could...

I'm so mad I could...

I'm so mad I could...

I'm so mad I could...

WRITE AND DRAW MORE OF YOUR OWN.

I'm so mad I could...

I'm so mad I could...

I'm so mad I could...

I'm so mad I could...

I'm so mad I could...

I'm so mad I could...

SCRIBBLE-TASTIC!

Feeling *SPIKEY*? Use this page to scribble your anger away.

Press as hard as you like –
without going through the paper.

THE FEELINGS FORT

Being alone doesn't have to be lonely. Sometimes if you're feeling angry or sad it's good to have some space.

Why not make yourself a feelings fort – a den where you can go if you want some time by yourself?

You could use chairs, sheets, cushions, or a space behind a desk.

Use the space below to imagine what your perfect den would be like.

MY BUGBEARS

Bugbears are things that annoy or irritate you. Write anything that makes you fed up on these bugs and imagine them flitting away or strolling off into the forest never to be seen again.

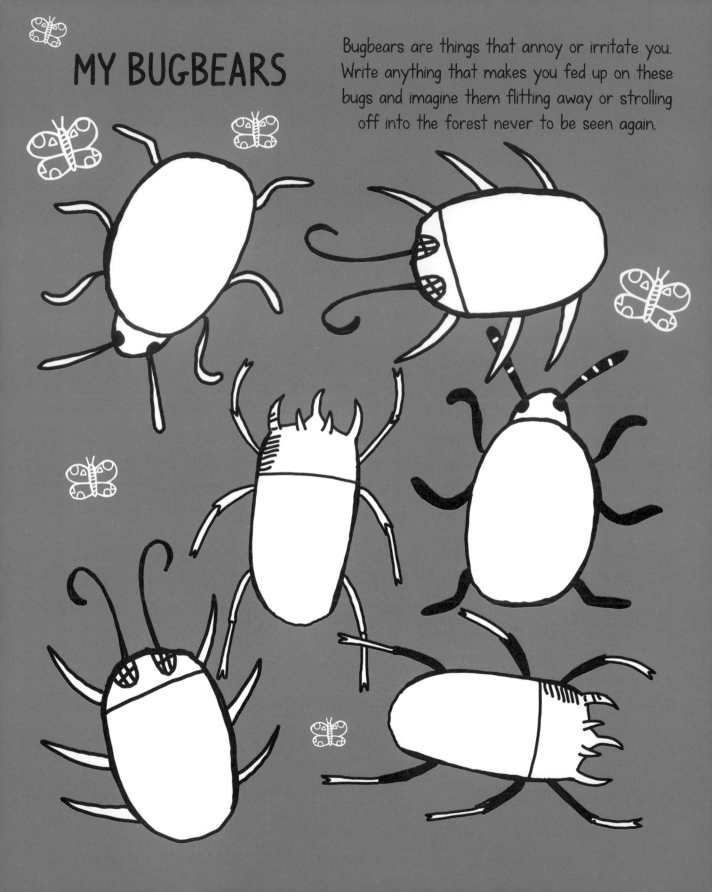

GRRR! I CAN'T BEAR IT WHEN...

COLOUR THIS IN

LIFE CAN BE GREAT

TIME TO LEARN

When we're angry we're not always thinking straight. It can be useful to learn some techniques to help you feel calmer.

BUDDY BREATHING

Lie down somewhere quiet and calm. Place your favourite cuddly toy on your tummy. Breathe in deeply to the count of 2 and then out to the count of 2. Watch as your cuddly friend rises and falls with your breath. Repeat this for 2 minutes.

ARGUING IN FUNNY VOICES

Practise some funny voices or mimic your favourite cartoon characters or celebrities. Next time you're mid argument, try switching to that voice and see what happens.

STOP, DROP, CURL, BREATHE

A good technique to distract yourself from angry feelings is the 'Stop, Drop' action. In the middle of an angry episode you should tell yourself to stop, drop down to the floor, curl up in a ball and focus on your breathing. This may seem weird, but if you can crack it, it can really help.

KITES

Try imagining sad memories which make you feel angry as kites on strings. Think about how they may tug at you from time to time but you have the power to control them. Or, if they are too much, you could simply release the string and let them fly away. Practise seeing these memories in this way.

YOU CRACK ME UP

Imagine your job involves making crackers for all your friends and family. What do you find funny? Fill the cracker slips with jokes, stories or funny memories.

GREAT GIFTS

Take some time to think about the people, pets and special friends you love and who love you.
Who would you like to thank in your life and why?

Write a message on each gift tag.

TO: ....
BECAUSE: ....
....

TO: ....
BECAUSE: ....
....

TO: ....
BECAUSE: ....
....

TO: ....
BECAUSE: ....
....

TO: ....
BECAUSE: ....
....

TO: . . . .

BECAUSE: . . . .

. . . .

TO: . . . .

BECAUSE: . . . .

. . . .

TO: . . . .

BECAUSE: . . . .

. . . .

TO: . . . .

BECAUSE: . . . .

. . . .

Write a message
on each gift tag.

TO: . . . .

BECAUSE: . . . .

. . . .

TO: . . . .

BECAUSE: . . . .

. . . .

SUPER PALS

You might not always think so, but you are super! Just ask your friends. Draw yourself and your best friend as superheroes and think of all your super characteristics.

Write your super characteristics down. Your friend should do the same on the next page.

Remind yourself why you are friends.

I am ....'s friend because ....

....

.... is my friend because

....

Remind yourself why you are friends.

Maybe you are funny, clever or a good friend.

If you have trouble thinking of your own super qualities, just swap sides and write about each other!

HELLO SADNESS

How does your sadness feel?
Use this page to put words to it.

Perhaps it feels like something heavy is sitting in your chest or throat. Perhaps it gives you an empty feeling.

WHEN I'M SAD I WANT TO...

Write some words or draw a picture to illustrate the way it feels.

I NEED...

I FEEL LIKE...

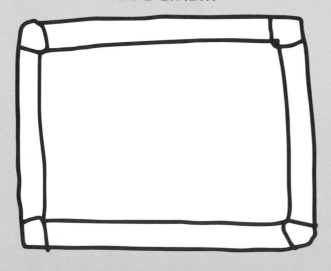

HELLO HAPPY

Read through these
5 steps and have a go.

Did you know you
can conjure up some
happy feelings for
yourself, right here,
right now?

1. Lie or sit somewhere
comfortable and quiet.

2. Close your eyes.

3. Think about a time in your
life when you were really happy
about something – maybe you
had a lovely day out, someone
was kind to you or you won a
certificate or prize.

4. Try to see yourself at that
time – think about what you
were wearing, the sights and
sounds of the place. How do
you feel being there?

5. Hold that picture in your mind
for as long as possible.

Use this space to stick a photograph
of yourself doing something that made
you happy, or draw a picture of you in
the future doing something you love.

YOU DID IT!
Now you've aced this exercise, practise
it whenever you like, to remind you
that you can feel happy and even
bring a smile to your face.

WHY SO SAD?

Lots of things can make us sad. Look at the pictures and colour in any of the things affecting you.

MOVING AWAY

NOT FITTING IN

BULLYING

FRIENDSHIP ISSUES

LOSS OF A LOVED ONE
RiP

SHYNESS

DIVORCE

SCHOOL ISSUES

Sometimes having to follow someone else's rules can make us feel sad or angry. Amuse yourself by colouring this picture outside the lines or smudging the ink.

MAVERICK MARKS

BALLOON POP

Go on, you know you want to. Pop the balloons by poking a hole in each with your pencil.

IN A WORD

Can you sum up the thing that's bothering you or your feelings in a word? If so, fill this page with that one word.

Write it big, small, upside down, and back to front.

SAD LION, HAPPY LION

This lion is sad. He doesn't like being cooped up.

Use the right hand
page to set him free.
Where does he go?
What does he do?

PILLOW PALS

It's good to have a friend and sometimes you need a special pal who doesn't talk but listens. Follow the step-by-step instructions to make a pillow pal who will love a squishy hug.

YOU WILL NEED:

One clean, dry white pillow case
Permanent fabric markers
Scraps of fabric or fleece (optional)
Pins
Scissors (optional)
Needle and cotton (optional)
One pillow

WHAT TO DO:

1. Take one clean, dry, white pillowcase.

2. Lay the pillowcase flat on a table or flat surface.

3. Think about the kind of pillow pal you would like – you could have a puppy, a cat or a doll. Choose something you love.

4. Use your magic markers to draw the eyes, nose and mouth of your new pal.

5. Draw two ear shapes on the reverse side of the scraps of fabric or fleece.

6. Cut them out.

7. Pin the ears on at either side of the eyes and sew the tops into place on the pillowcase. This will allow you to play with the floppy ears. (If you don't have fabric just draw the ears on instead.)

8. Put the pillow back in the pillowcase. Your pillow pal is ready for hugs!

Remember! Scissors and needles are sharp.

Ask a grown-up to help with this craft.

Want to do something different?

Why not write the word **Friends** on your pillow and add your best friends names.

Or, ask your pals to write a friendly message to you that you can read whenever you like.

YOU'RE AMAZING!

You may not think so but you're amazing. Pick 3 of these statements which most apply to you.

I am adventurous

I am a
good listener

I am interesting

I am reliable

I am kind

I am alive

I am strong

I am
patient

I am funny

I am loyal

I am
determined

I am clever

I am
open-minded

I am
honest

I am full of promise

Write them on the notepad and repeat them every day.

MIRROR, MIRROR

It's hard to feel happy if your self-confidence is low.

Find a mirror, sit in front of it and study yourself.

Find something, however small it seems, that you like about yourself and repeat it out loud to yourself in a confident voice. It could be anything - here are some ideas.

I have thick eyelashes.

I like the way my nose wrinkles when I smile.

My freckles are cute.

My fingernails are a nice shape.

HELPING HAND

Being kind and helpful to others makes us feel good.

Now's the time to remind yourself of the fact that you're a kind person and there are lots of kind people in the world.

Place one hand on this page and draw around it.

On each finger write down a time when you've helped someone.

On the palm of the right hand jot down a time when someone has helped you.

Place your foot on this page and draw around it.

WALK IN MY SHOES

When you feel really angry or sad it's easy to feel you are on your own. But, there is always someone who will listen and do their best to understand what you are going through.

On each toe, write the name of someone you can ask for help when you're feeling sad or angry.

END OF THE RAINBOW

Rainbows always make us feel good. What would you love to find at the end of this one?

DEAR X...

Use this page to write a letter to someone who has made you sad or angry

When you have finished tear it out. You could rip it up and throw it away or bury it in the garden.

Now you've voiced those feelings you can move on.

Today is going to be a good day!
You can sometimes alter your mood and outlook just by thinking positively.

TODAY'S THE DAY

Write down some things you're going to enjoy doing today.

STAIRWAY TO HAPPY

Setting a goal and working towards it is a great way to make yourself feel good.

CHECK OUT
THIS STAIRCASE

Yes, I did it!

I don't want to do it!

Write your goal on the top step and draw yourself on to each step whenever you move towards positive action.

SURF'S UP!

Emotions are like waves, they build up,
crash over us and then wash away.

Draw the sea on an angry day.

Now, draw the sea on a calm day.

LITTLE JAR OF AWESOME

1. Find an empty jar with a lid.
2. Decorate it with pens or stickers.
3. Keep it somewhere safe.

Whenever something good, fun or downright awesome happens in your life write it on a scrap of paper and put it in the jar.

You could open the jar and read the contents on a weekly basis, on a special day like your birthday or New Year's Eve or whenever you feel low.

DITSY DOODLES

Catch yourself on a calm day.
Let your happiness spread across
the page as you doodle.

PAY IT FORWARD

You've probably heard of paying someone back by returning a good deed, but have you ever heard of paying it forward?

This is the idea that you make the world a better place by doing small, random acts of kindness for other people and make yourself happier in the process.

Use this page to think of the ways you could make someone's day.

It could be anything from holding a door open, introducing yourself to the new boy or girl at school or cleaning out your wardrobe and donating old clothes to charity.

Make yourself and your family feel good by sticking reminder notes around the house with positive, kind and lovely messages on them.

FRIENDLY WISHES

Use the spaces here to test out some thoughts before you transfer them on to sticky notes.

Music can really lift your mood. Use this page to make a lyrics poster for a song which makes your spirits soar. Write the words and add some cheery doodles. Or, write a playlist of all the different tracks which help you feel happy.

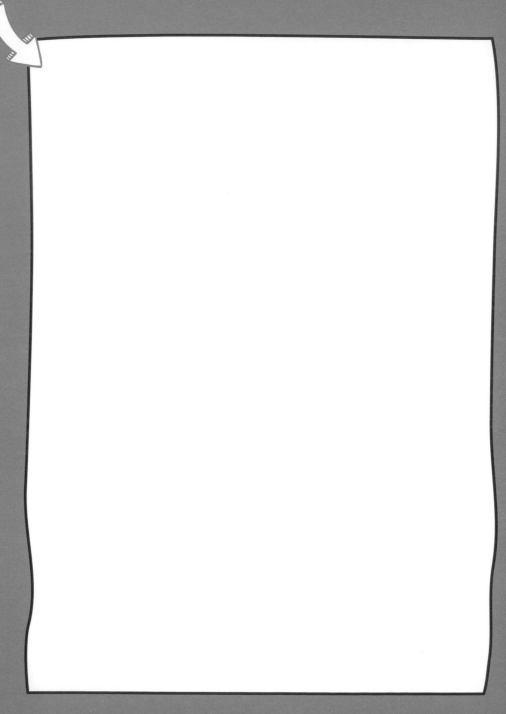

YOUR GO!

Use this page to write down words or sentences about your feelings. Can you turn these into lyrics for a poem or song?

LAUGH IT UP!

When we laugh our body relaxes and endorphins – natural chemicals which make us feel good – are released into our bloodstream. Laughing is brilliant fun even though we might at first have to fake it.

Think of your favourite animal and then try laughing as you imagine they would. Snort like a piggy, woof like a dog, caterwaul like a cat, hee-haw like a donkey, screech like a monkey or yak like a hyena.

Imagine yourself laughing at different ages. How did you laugh as a baby? As a 3-year-old? How will you laugh when you are double your age? What about when you are 80?

Laugh like your teacher has just cancelled all homework... forever!

Laugh like an evil overlord who's just taken over the universe. Mwa ha ha ha!

Now laugh like Santa Claus.

With a friend, grab a feather duster or something equally ticklish and try to get each other to laugh.

Play the 'moo' game. Grab a friend or sibling and try to make each other laugh by moo-ing at them.

WHEN I LAUGH MY TUMMY FEELS

....

....

MY HEAD FEELS

....

....

MY HEART FEELS

....

....

....

LAUGH-O
METER

'SUP!

Where's your glass today? Is it half full or half empty?

	AM	PM
MONDAY		
TUESDAY		
WEDNESDAY		
THURSDAY		
FRIDAY		
SATURDAY		
SUNDAY		

Fill each glass as you go through the week.

Add notes about why you were feeling more or less hopeful and cheerful on each day.

SMELL AND TELL

Focusing on our senses can help us be in the moment and calm angry or sad emotions.

Play this game with an adult.

Keep your eyes firmly closed. The adult should pass you something fragrant, like a piece of orange peel, or something nice to touch, like a feather.

Keeping your eyes tight shut, really focus on how the object smells or feels.

You could play this game with a group of friends and take it in turns to use your senses.

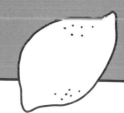

OUT OF IDEAS? TRY ONE OF THESE...

a feather	a sprig of lavender	a cube of jelly	some coffee beans
a pine cone	a pebble	a dressing gown cord	a blob of toothpaste
a banana	a plastic piece of cutlery	a cup of rice	a freshly washed piece of laundry
a pencil	a cuddly toy	a piece of ribbon	a lemon or a lime
a piece of fluff	a rock	a lump of modelling clay	a plastic brick
a rose petal	a deflated balloon	a squirt of perfume on a piece of paper	a leaf
a sprig of rosemary	a shell		

THANKS A BUNCH!

Feeling thankful for the things we have, can help us feel less sad about our problems and worries. Here's how to make a thankful tree to remind yourself of the good things in your life.

YOU WILL NEED:

A jam jar or small vase

Stickers or ribbon for decoration (optional)

Long twigs or skinny branches

Pen or pencil

Coloured paper

Scissors

Hole punch

String, twine, thread or ribbon

Scissors are sharp! Ask a grown up to help with this craft.

WHAT TO DO:

You don't have to add all the leaves in one go, you could save them and add them as you think of things you're grateful for.

1. First, collect twigs or thin branches from your garden or park. Remember, don't cut live plants without permission.

2. Decorate your jar or vase. Add stickers or tie a piece of pretty ribbon around the neck.

3. Place the cluster of twigs inside the jar, as you would with a bunch of flowers. Your tree is now ready.

4. Cut the leaves out with the scissors.

5. Write down something you're thankful for on each leaf. Then punch a hole in one end of them.

6. Tie each leaf to a branch using lengths of string, thread or ribbon.

If you don't have a jar or twigs, why not draw a trunk and branches on a big piece of paper and stick the leaves on with glue.

FILL THIS HEART WITH HAPPY

SAY WHAT?

When's the last time you gave
or received a compliment?

Recall some nice things people
have said to you and write
them in the speech bubbles.

Now write some ideas for compliments you could give others in these bubbles.

JUST A TOUCH OF LOVE

We have five senses for a reason and touch is one of the best.

Touch helps us connect with our surroundings and feel better about our world.

Here are some brilliant ways to get touchy-feely.

Stroke an animal. Maybe you have a pet. If not, ask a dog-owner if you can give their pet a stroke.

Hold hands with your best friend.

Have a hug – this might be with a friend or family member or someone you love and trust.

Cuddle a fleecy blanket or your favourite soft, cuddly toy.

Next time you're on the sofa watching tv, have a foot massage. Ask a parent or carer if they can give your feet a rub with or without your socks on.

CREATE A CALMING KIT

Imagine having your own kit to help you feel calm and peaceful. Well, you can easily make one to house all the things which give you a happy fix.

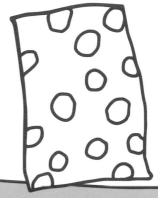

Start by taking a gift box or shoe box or a little bag. You could decorate this if you like. You'll be using it to store your special things.

Now hunt around the house to find things you enjoy touching, smelling or hearing. It could even be something you just smile at the sight of.

HERE ARE SOME IDEAS...
WHAT WILL YOU INCLUDE?

a scrap of silky fabric
a small bouncy ball
an old photograph
a scented rubber
a tinkling toy bell
a wrapped sweet
a bird's feather

Keep your calming kit somewhere safe and bring it out whenever you feel low, angry or anxious.

ALTERNATIVE ACTIONS

WHAT HAPPENED

One day...

Just then...

In the end...

WHAT HAPPENED

One day...

Just then...

In the end...

WHAT HAPPENED

One day...

Just then...

In the end...

Use this page to sketch out some examples of times when you were angry and bad things happened as a consequence. Think about what you could have done differently and then sketch that and the difference it may have made, on the next strip.

WHAT I COULD DO DIFFERENTLY

One day...	Just then...	In the end...

WHAT I COULD DO DIFFERENTLY

One day...	Just then...	In the end...

WHAT I COULD DO DIFFERENTLY

One day...	Just then...	In the end...

ANIMAL INSTINCTS

Taking a walk on the wild side can really help you when you're feeling low.

Use this page to think about how you can bring animals into your life.

Looking after your pet's needs and training them can take focus off any negative feelings you may be having.

FISHY FRIENDS

Research shows that watching fish swim can have a calming effect. If you don't have your own fish tank, ask your parent to take you to see fish in a pond or an aquarium.

DOG'S LIFE

Pups are brilliant fun. If you have a dog make sure you're first in line to sign up for grooming and dog-walking duties.

PET CARE

Pets take a lot of work but are very rewarding. If you don't have your own pet maybe you could help look after a pal or family member's furry or feathery friend.

PET CARE

Why not entice wildlife to your garden, yard or balcony. Planting flowers in pots encourages bees and butterflies. Hang a bird feeder to attract birds or put out some cat or dog food for your friendly neighbourhood hedgehog.

You could even line a box with newspaper and dry bedding for the hedgehog to hibernate undisturbed all winter.

FEELING BLUE?

How does the world look when you're sad? Use shades of blue, turquoise, aqua, navy or black to colour this picture.

OUT AND ABOUT

Getting out and about can really help banish boredom and boost your mood.

Next time you're feeling low, grab your coat and head outside in the fresh air.

Check out the ideas on this page and give them a go.

LOCAL LOOKOUT

STOP

Walks can seem dull if you're wandering aimlessly, but not if you've got your super-senses attuned to everything around you.

Draw a grid like the one below on a piece of paper or card. You'll need one for each person you're with. Take the papers and pencils and go on a 'noticing' walk.

Tick off each item when you see it.

ITEM	FOUND!	ITEM	FOUND!
Post box	☐	Church	☐
Butterfly	☐	Tin can	☐
Stop sign	☐	Cat	☐
Carrier bag	☐	Lorry	☐
For Sale sign	☐	Airplane	☐
Goal post	☐	Rosebush	☐

SOUND SAFARI

Now try a Sound Safari. Draw a grid like the one below on a piece of paper or card. You'll need one for each person you're with.

ITEM	FOUND!	ITEM	FOUND!
Birdsong	☐	A beeping car horn	☐
A dog barking	☐	Someone shouting	☐
The wind	☐	Children playing	☐
The rain	☐	Music	☐
A door slamming	☐	Running footsteps	☐
A fire engine, ambulance or police car siren	☐	A clock or bell chiming	☐

LA LA LA

Take paper and a pencil and go on a Sound Safari. Tick off each sound when you hear it.

DING DONG

ONE WORD

Think of your favourite word and write it in the space below. It could be a word that makes you feel happy, or a word that you like the sound of when you speak it out loud.

LITTLE JAR OF STRENGTH

Find an an empty jar with a lid. Decorate it with pens or stickers. Every time you think of a strength write it on a scrap of paper and put it in the jar. Keep it somewhere safe.

GOOD STUFF GRID

Banish bad thoughts at bedtime. Add one hundred things which make you smile to this grid.

movies

You don't have to fill it all at once, just add something when it pops into your head.

...ice-creams, football, walks on the beach, hula-hoops, furry tigers, mashed potato...

SLEEP TIGHT

Getting a good night's sleep can really help your mood. Here's how to give yourself the best chance of some quality zzzzzz's.

NOM NOM

Have a bedtime snack which combines protein and carbs, like milk and muesli or toast and peanut butter. Don't forget to brush your teeth afterwards.

LIGHTS OUT

The healthiest way to sleep is in complete darkness, so turn your lights off. If you're too scared to sleep in the dark, keep the door open and switch the landing light on or keep a night light on.

SWITCH OFF AND UNPLUG

Watching TV, playing on a smart phone and tablet or playing video games before bed is bad news as your brain will be racing. Turn all screens off an hour before bedtime and turn devices off at the plug.

BUBBLES AND SNUGGLES

A warm bubbly bath and a cosy towel are a great way to help you feel sleepy. Ask your parent or carer to read you a story and you'll be drifting off to dreamland before you know it.

Draw a picture of a dream you'd enjoy having.

You could base this on a real-life, happy memory or create something new.

Remember, it's a dream so it can be as crazy and fantastical as you like.

OH THE PLACES YOU'LL GO...

The world's a big place full of endless possibilities.

Write down some ideas of the places you'll visit and things you hope to do in the future.

JAR OF LIFE

Making good choices about how to spend our lives is really important.

This exercise helps you understand about priorities and how putting the important things first helps make life more happy and fulfilling.

You will need:

A big jar
A bowl of sand
A bowl of small pebbles
A bowl of big rocks

In this game:

The jar represents your life.

The rocks are the really important things that money can't buy like your family, your friends, your health, your goals and doing what you love.

The pebbles are the things that matter and are important, but aren't necessarily vital like homework, your hobbies, seeing people who aren't really your friends.

The sand is the things that don't really matter, like video games, your smart phone, being mad at people.

First fill the jar with the sand, then the pebbles. You will see you don't have room for all the big rocks.

This shows that if you concentrate too much on the things that don't really matter, you'll have less time for the things that are really important.

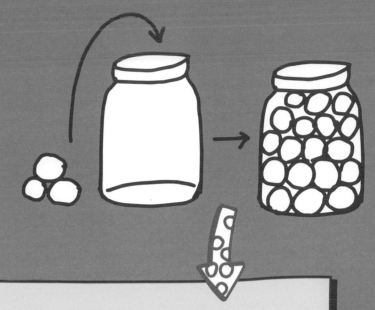

Empty the jar and sort the contents back into sand, pebbles and rocks. Now, try again. This time fill the jar with the rocks first, then the pebbles and lastly the sand.

You'll find that the pebbles and sand will fill up the gaps between the rocks and you'll fit much more in.

This shows that if you concentrate on the important things first and fill gaps in your time with things which matter less and don't really matter at all, you will have time to do everything in life.

THE BIT FOR GROWN UPS

This activity book is perfect for parents, teachers, learning mentors, caregivers, therapists and youth leaders who want to help children to understand and leave behind their worries.

Modern life for our children can be highly stressful, and feel like it's all about being popular and successful. We know that they experience many internal and external pressures, for example comparing themselves with others around them and feeling they aren't good enough which can lead to anger.

Children are very resilient and, in a loving and nurturing environment, will often work through problems and difficult times without needing additional help. This book offers the chance for your child to explore, express and explain their worries and open up the conversation with you. The fun activities build resilience, increase inner calm, improve understanding of emotions and encourage positivity.

When children feel stuck in sadness or anger, they may become lonely and isolated, and struggle to make sense of what is happening because they don't have the language to explain their distress. You might notice a decline in self esteem and confidence along with complaints of tummy aches, headaches or feeling exhausted and avoidance of previously enjoyed activities.

If your child's distress or anger persist beyond 3 months or escalate rather than decrease, you can talk to their school, your GP, a counsellor or one of the organisations listed below.

YOUNG MINDS PARENT HELPLINE

Call weekdays 9.30am to 4pm – free in England, Scotland, Wales and N. Ireland

Call to talk through your child's problem. Advisers will listen to your concerns and questions in complete confidentiality, help you to understand your child's behaviour and give you practical advice on where to go next. If you need further help, they'll refer you to a specialist, e.g. a psychotherapist, psychiatrist, psychologist or a mental health nurse within 7 days.

Tel: 0808 802 5544   www.youngminds.org.uk

MIND – FOR BETTER MENTAL HEALTH

Mind's team provides information on a range of topics including: types of mental health problem, where to get help, medication and alternative treatments and advocacy. They will look for details of help and support in your own area.

Call weekdays 9am to 6pm. Phone calls from UK landlines are charged at local rates. Charges from mobile telephones vary considerably.

Tel: 0300 123 3393   Text: 86463
www.mind.org.uk

SANE HELPLINE

SANE's helpline is a national, 7 days a week, out-of-hours (4.30pm to 10.30pm) telephone helpline for anyone coping with mental illness, including concerned relatives or friends.

Tel: 0300 304 7000
www.sane.org.uk

DR. SHARIE COOMBES